The Legend of the Mimigwesseos

ADAM BALLANTYNE

The Legend of the Mimigwesseos

Transcribed and edited by PRENTICE G. DOWNES
Introduction by ROBERT COCKBURN
Woodcuts by
ANNIE DOWNES CATTERSON

PENUMBRA PRESS

Published by Penumbra Press
Printed and bound in Canada by AGMV-Marquis
The text stock is Rolland Opaque Cream and the type is Palatino

CANADIAN CATALOGUING IN PUBLICATION DATA

Ballantyne, Adam
The Legend of the Mimigwesseos

ISBN 0-921254-80-6

1. Cree Indians-- Folklore. 2. Legends--Canada.
I. Catterson, Annie Downes II. Downes, P.G. (Prentice Gilbert), 1909-1959. III. Title.

E99.C88B33 1988 j398.2′097101 C98-901381-2

For my mother, E.G.,
and to the people of Pelican Narrows

Introduction

ROBERT COCKBURN

TALKING BEARS; MOOSE THAT LIVED UNDER WATER; THE TRICKSTER GOD named Wisakyjak, who created the animal kingdom; the blackened, lipless, fanged cannibals known as "witigos" — all these beings and others as wonderfully strange once inhabited northern Manitoba and Saskatchewan, the homeland of the Woodland Cree. So too did 'mimigwesseos'. They lived among rocks on islands and in the ledges and cliffs of lakes and rivers; elf-like creatures with flat, noseless faces, they were sometimes helpful but were dangerous to meddle with. This book is about them.

It is about them, the vast, water-laced boreal forest where they led their secret lives, and the Indians who sometimes saw and always feared them. They are gone now, the mimigwesseos; gone with the underwater moose and the talking animals and the terrifying witigos. But they were still alive only sixty years ago in the minds and recollections of Cree elders, men who remembered with reverence their people's traditional, immemorial beliefs and way of life. That centuries-old culture, with its own customs and legends, its own spiritual world, endured into the early twentieth century, but by the time the stories in this book were told and collected, Cree life had been altered drastically by Christian missionaries, the white man's economic practices, radio communication, and air travel. Even so, much remained that seemed timeless, and it was the allure of a still-vibrant hunting culture and all that it entailed — language, lore, beliefs — that drew a young American schoolmaster to northern Saskatchewan in the years before the outbreak of the Second World War.

From 1936 to 1940 Prentice G. Downes spent his summers travelling by canoe from the Churchill River country north to the rim of the

Barren Lands, whenever possible in the company of Indians. His starting point for these trips, and the place to which he returned when they ended, was Pelican Narrows, Saskatchewan, home of the Peter Ballantyne Band of the Woodland Cree. It was there, in 1937, that he met Adam Ballantyne, a 75-year-old 'medicine man' who was to teach him much about Cree life and lore. Through Native interpreters, for he did not fully trust his understanding of the Cree tongue, Downes made it known that he had come a great distance to "learn the things of long ago, because," he wrote in his journal, "I knew they were being fast forgotten and thought that they should be written down before they had all disappeared and no person would any longer be able to remember them or how his forefathers lived." Adam, who had never accepted the white man's treaty or his religion, occupied a

curious position in the band. Though the younger people were inclined to ridicule his beliefs, still, when anyone was really ill, when all the white man's nostrums, pain-killers, and pills were of no avail, they would turn to the old medicine man.... He is a very exact narrator and is extremely careful to correct errors. His stories were repeated after they had been given to me in summary, and [he regularly] corrected ideas or misinterpretations. He made a sharp distinction between what was fact and what was considered as fancy.... Crouched with his toes tucked under him, he would gesticulate and sometimes become very excited, sweating, and rocking back and forth with emotional recollection.

"Things were very different long ago, before religion," the oracle told Downes.

For then there was no sin, then there was no *fear*, and people were happy; happy like the animals, and a man was satisfied.... Long ago, Peter Ballantyne, my grandfather, who was first chief of this band, told me of these things which I tell you so that they may not be forgotten. I have two sons, and when I tell them, they laugh. But Peter told me these things, which I learned before I was twenty-five. And many of these things I know to be true, for I have done them and seen them.... These matters and the old days are clearer to me than today. I can see them like words of fire in my head; I can see the very things I am telling you about, for you do not laugh at these things which Peter told me and his father told him.

So it was that an enthralled Downes spent many hours listening, questioning, and writing down what he heard, in sunshine, under rain-tapping canvas, and in the red light of campfires as Adam told about "these things": about hunting, fishing, and trapping skills; natural medicine; taboos and portents; games; bear-worship; the meaning of the northern lights; scapulamancy; and the spirit-world of the Cree, what we would call their mythology, to which the mimigwesseos belonged. As Downes remarks in *Sleeping Island*, his classic book of northern travel, "to the Cree mind, all the world was spirit-bearing and animistic — every tree, every animal, every insect, and even the rocks and sand and water. His life was spent in placating and observing a host of spirits. He and the world about him were a completely dual world of the physical and its spirit counterpart." So it was that Adam explained to Downes how "the old men, long years ago, went to the mimigwesseos for their medicine," and exactly how they obtained it. "This is true," he insisted, "for I have done so and have some of this medicine in my tent. Sometimes one can hear the mimigwesseos laughing in the cliffs."

Downes' respect and liking for Adam was reciprocated; the young outsider's profound interest in Cree culture made such an impression on the venerable raconteur that he regretted Downes had been baptized: "He was quite confident that if this had not happened, under his tutelage and with the use of the proper drum, I should have been capable, in time, of communication with him when I went away to the unknown south in the fall." The two men met briefly in 1939 but not at all in 1940, after which Downes was kept away by the war. Seven years passed before he returned, but when he canoed into

Pelican Narrows in 1947 he found Adam still robust and as eager as ever to share his knowledge of "long ago." His notebook open and an interpreter at his side, the American resumed from where he had left off with Adam; these were rewarding days. Finally the evening of departure arrived and "Adam came over for a cup of tea and a good-bye and a little chat." As he pushed off in his canoe, Downes did not know that he would never see the village or the old man again. "The lake had scarcely a ripple.... And Pelican was at last lost to view. I thought I saw Adam watching from his tent, but I could not be sure."

The Legend of the Mimigwesseos is the third book of Cree stories told to P.G. Downes to be illustrated by his daughter, Annie Downes Catterson; it follows *The Story of Chakapas* (1987) and *Wisakyjak and the New World* (1991), which were also published by Penumbra Press. As she did in those books, Annie has drawn upon her father's unpublished collections of Cree lore and mythology in presenting this group of stories. In so doing she honours the heartfelt tribute he paid Adam Ballantyne and his many other Indian friends in *Sleeping Island*. These strange mimigwesseos tales are made all the more otherworldly by the prints that accompany them, for Annie Downes Catterson's brilliant woodcuts express an imaginative and emotional affinity with the spirit world of the Woodland Cree. Her pictures also remind us, palpably, that in that culture the supernatural was indivisible from the natural; turning these pages, we can smell that northern wilderness — cold water, ice, poplar and black spruce, woodsmoke — and feel in our bones the stories that Adam Ballantyne heard from his grandfather more than a century ago.

And now, before I tell you any more, I must tell you about the forest. In the forest in which we have always lived, lived forever and forever, in many ways all is magic. We think of it as the greatest forest in the world, and indeed I cannot imagine a place where there is no forest, for here everywhere you look and walk are the trees. And everywhere you look are the many lakes and rivers, but over all the land stretches the forest. It is a forest of spruce trees, always green, though sometimes the winter snows are so great as to almost completely hide some of the small ones. Far away, I am told, far away to the north where the 'raw meat eaters' live, 'Ask-y-mo' we call them, they tell me that trees become smaller and smaller and then finally disappear, but this is a land I have never seen. How can a man live without the trees?

The forest trees have always provided us with many things we need. From the spruce, first of all comes our fire to keep us warm and cook our food. From its needles we make a tea to use when we are sick. From the roots we make a kind of string used to sew up the bark on our birch bark canoes. From the gum of the spruce, we make a sort of glue that you use to repair the canoe when it has a hole in it. From the wonderful white birch, we make our baskets. From the little brown growths on the bark we make a powder which we use to start a fire. Long, long ago from the bark of the birch, we sometimes made our houses. From it too, we make the frame for our snowshoes. You see,
I cannot understand how any people can live in a land where there are no trees such as ours.

If you could be like the birds and fly high above the forest, you would see a wonderful world. Everywhere you could look as far as the horizon. In every direction you would see nothing but the forest, nothing but millions and millions of trees, no roads, no houses, no cities, only the forest and shining here and there, the beautiful clear lakes or maybe the white flash of some great waterfall or rapid.

But there are more than trees, for in the forest live we people, and in the forest too, are our friends the many different animals, our friends the many different birds. And to each the forest is their home; without the forest they could not live.

We believe that all living things in the forest have a spirit of their own. We believe they live and talk and think all in their own language. there are many strange sounds in the forest because of this. Sometimes when you are deep in the woods you must sit very still and close your eyes and if you listen very carefully for a long time you will hear many things. You will hear the trees talking, this is a sound far above the ground. You may hear the wind coming from far away. You may hear a strange humming which is all the insects talking together. You may hear some tired tree groaning for it is so old that it hurts when the wind is rough and bends it more than it wishes. You may hear many things, the ground itself may talk with the thump-thump of a running rabbit, or the sharp quick thump of a deer as he paws the ground to get at a mushroom. And you will have all the different sounds of the birds calling to each other or they may be just talking to each other in their own language.

And if you listen enough, all these sounds which sound so strange at first will become friendly to you. You will know what they mean, and you will feel at last as we do, that once in the forest you are under the good spirits and friendliness of the wondrous trees, and that is your home and protection from all the rest of the world, for here among man's oldest friends, the trees, the world of men when it is cruel or unkind can never find you; and the forest provides all that you may need.

And when you go through the forest, you may think that no one sees you and that you are all alone. Such is not true, as we well know, for the beings of the forest, the fox, a rabbit here, a squirrel there, a bird, a mouse, and the trees themselves, all of them notice your passing and each one tells the others in some way. As you brush against a branch it calls out and this tells the squirrel and the squirrel chatters and this tells the bluejay and the bluejay calls out and this tells the other birds, and thus the rabbit knows and as he runs, thump, thump, the fox who listens very sharply is told and he may call out and so does the deer know, and so you see all the animals and trees know that you are there. This is part of the magic of the forest.

Think then for a moment of this wonderful world. Sometimes it is so green and bright, sometimes it looks almost blue. Sometimes the clouds are making dark shadows on it and then in winter it has a thousand sparkling diamonds from the ice. And it rolls on and on forever as far as I know.

Imagine that you are here with me now as I tell you these stories, we are sitting beside the shore of a great lake. It is near sunset and the western sky has turned all yellow. All around us is the friendly forest; turning from green to dark blue and then purple before the sun at last goes down. We have a little fire before us. The lake is very calm and peaceful. It too has been dyed yellow by the sunset. The last of the small birds are calling. Far out in the still lake a little circle forms, it is a fish sticking up his nose to catch a wandering fly which has lighted on the water. Far away you may hear the strange and beautiful call of mahgua, the loon. This means, he tells us, that there will be wind tomorrow. But all is so quiet and peaceful and beautiful now. For a long while we say nothing; just listen to the forest talk. So now I must tell you more and what I tell you now is about the Mimigwesseos.*

* pronounced *Mee-mee-guay-see-o-s*

In the days of long ago, which I have been telling you about, there lived a very strange little people whom we still talk about and which are known among many of the northern forest people. These are what we call the Mimigwesseos. These Mimigwesseos were a very small people. They lived in the rocks or in caves in the rocks, usually near waterfalls and always near some sort of water, a stream, a river, maybe a great lake.

These little people had many magical powers; indeed it would seem they were magic itself. They were only about three or four feet high and had the most peculiar faces. For their faces were almost flat, and they had nearly no nose at all, just two holes for nostrils. They seemed rather embarrassed by this, and when you would come upon them, they would crouch down, bow their heads and bury their faces in their hands so you could not see they had no real nose.

My wife's grandfather saw some Mimigwesseos long ago. In those days, he used to make trips down the Saskatchewan River. As he was passing by a cliff, he heard talking inside the rock. He knew that this must come from Mimigwesseos. It was a morning in the spring, and there was a mist all over the water. He visited his nets which he had placed near this cliff. They were all torn and twisted as if fish had been caught in them, and yet there were no fish. As he dropped the net back into the water he looked up. There, dimly outlined through the mist, he saw a small canoe, and in it three small people. They were bent over and had their hands over their faces. They were singing a very strange song in high quavering voices. It went:

"Pali ... pali ... pali...."

Then the canoe moved on through the mist right into the great cliff. He listened, and he could hear laughing and talking from within the cliff itself. Even the canoes of the Mimigwesseos were of stone, so the old people used to say, which would prove that these were magic people.

If you ask me if I believe in Mimigwesseos, I must tell you that I do, for as the wise people of long ago did, thus so do I now.

The old men, long years ago, used to go to the Mimigwesseos to get medicine. To do this they would go down into Deschambault Lake, which is not very far from where we sit now. There is a certain island in this lake which has a great steep rock. In this are many caves in which the Mimigwesseos lived, and at the bottom of the cliff are many great stones.

The old men would go to this island and to a certain landing spot which had been known for many generations. They then would lay a piece of moose hide down on the ground, a piece of hide about the size of a handkerchief. They would ask the Mimigwesseos for the type of medicine which they needed. It might be medicine for a pain in the back, for a pain in the arm or a pain in the head, but they must be sure and say exactly what kind of pain this medicine was to be used for.

Then they would go away. Several days later they would come back. There would be the piece of hide all tied up into a little bundle. Inside would be the medicine which they had asked for. It would be all powdered up and might be of any of several different colors. It would be all ready to use.

I myself, know this to be true for I have done exactly this thing only I used a cloth. Sure enough when I came back there was the cloth all tied up neatly into a little bundle and inside was the medicine. I have some of this medicine in my tent now.

I must tell you further about this island in Deschambault Lake where the Mimigwesseos lived, and where our fathers went to get their medicine. Well, no young woman was supposed to go to this island, but one day two young girls were paddling by the island, when one of them spied some fine white birch trees on the shore. Suddenly she wished very much to have the bark from one of these trees that she might make a basket. Despite the warnings of the other girl, she insisted upon going nearer to the island and finally persuaded her companion to leave her off on the shore for a few minutes. She stepped out of the canoe as it touched the shore and was soon lost from view behind a great stone. In a moment, a small scream was heard. Frightened, the other girl paddled away from the island. But the girl who had stepped ashore was never seen again.

Then twelve years later some men went to the island to seek medicine. There she was. They saw her amongst the rocks. But strangely, she was just as young and just as beautiful as when she had disappeared twelve years before. She smiled at the men but said nothing. She smiled and began to sing in a high girlish voice: "Pali ... pali ... pali...."

The men were frightened, and they went away. But that was long, long ago and no one has ever seen her since.

It seems that the Mimigwesseos were always found near water. It appears that they liked to eat fish. I remember hearing a story one day which would seem to prove that they preferred fish. A friend of mine used to live near Grand Rapids on the Saskatchewan River. Twice he set out his nets, and each time he found them twisted and torn and that they had been robbed of their fish. The third time he set out his nets he determined to return to them at an unexpected time that he might possibly catch whoever was robbing them. This he did. He came round the bend of the river silently and swiftly at an unusual hour of the day for one to get their nets. Coming thus upon his nets he was surprised to discover a little canoe there and in it two little dwarf-like people. They were so ashamed at being caught stealing from the nets that they bowed their heads and covered their faces with their hands and would not look at him.

However, realizing they were Mimigwesseos, he told them that he did not mind that they should take his fish. They said nothing but set off across the river (for here it widens to form a lake) and disappeared. They disappeared into the cliff. Later, he and his father came down again and examined the cliff very carefully. There was not a crack nor a cranny into which anything might have gone. After examining the cliff, they left a haunch of bear meat at the base of it and paddled off some distance and waited. Before long the meat began to move, and then it disappeared into the cliff. Suddenly the meat came whirling through the air right into their canoe, for it seems that the Mimigwesseos do not like meat, only fish.

Now I must tell you one final story about the Mimigwesseos. It is a rather long story, but we of the northern forests all know this story even today.

If you should ever travel north of here you might go up the great, clear, cold Reindeer River, or as we call it in our language, the 'Attik-seepee'. This is a wonderful river with very clear, very cold water, with rapids and falls, and many islands. There is one island above all others in this river just above a spot called Rocky Falls. This is a very round island, very round in shape and also in form so that, in a way, it looks like part of a head floating in the water. It is not a very large island, but it is an island upon which the Mimigwesseos lived.

Yes, and so it was many years ago when a canoe carrying three young men, three Indian boys, from a place called Lac-La-Ronge travelled up this river on their way north to some new hunting grounds. They had never been in this part of the country before, so possibly they did not know that this was a Mimigwesseos' island. It was in the late summer, and they were hurrying on their way (before the great fall winds should begin to blow) when they passed close to this island. As they passed by, they saw off at some distance a little canoe and in it three little people.

The young men began to paddle as hard as they could so that they, before long, had almost reached the little canoe. The little canoe, too, had been attempting to draw away from that of the young men, who were strong and eager and had soon quite overtaken the smaller one.

As they drew alongside the little canoe, they found that the three small people stopped paddling and bent over, hiding their faces in their hands. The young man in the bow of his canoe grasped the bow of the small canoe rather roughly and cried to the first of the little people:

"Tell me some news!"

This is a greeting that is often used among us. The first Mimigwesseo answered from amidst his hands:

"You will never see the snow fly!"

Then the second young man, he who was sitting in the middle of his canoe, said to the second Mimigwesseo:

"Tell me some news!"

The second Mimigwesseo, without raising his head, said:

"You will never see the new year!"

Then the third and last of the young men, he who was sitting in the stern said:

"Tell me some news!"

The last of the Mimigwesseos said:

"You will never see the spring!"

Then suddenly the little canoe sped away from the surprised young men, sped away and disappeared. But they went on their way to the north, laughing and joking about the strange little people and the strange things they had told them. They went on for many days, far up the Reindeer River, on across that great lake called Reindeer Lake, that great lake which is known to have some monstrously huge fish in it. Indeed, it is said that there is a fish in it so large that he can stick his head up through holes in the spring ice and swallow a caribou with one great bite.

Finally they reached a land where they thought they might well set out their traps. But somehow a quarrel broke out among them, a quarrel which became so violent that finally one of the young men, he who had been the first to ask the Mimigwesseos for news, was killed.

Frightened at this event, the other two left their trap line and turned back; for this quarrel occurred just a day before the first snowstorm of the year. Hurrying south, one of them, he who had been in the middle of the canoe, became lost while hunting a week or so before the very end of the year. He wandered about and starved to death. The final one, now very terrified, managed to get back to Lac-La-Ronge. There, just before the ice melted that spring, he died from having eaten some moose meat that was bad. Thus, you see, one must not laugh when they meet a Mimigwesseo. All the old people around here know this story.

And now, friend of mine, the fire is burning very low. Just the wonderful glowing coals, and I see a tiny blue flame. Ah! There will be cold tomorrow. The great stars are in the sky. Far to the north, I see the cluster of stars you call the Little Dipper and we call the Otter. I can see stretching across the heavens the Bird's Path. Here in the blackness of the night soon we will see the spirits dancing. These you call the Northern Lights; these we know are the spirits of all happy people who have departed, who are now dancing here in the sky. These we call the 'Cheepai'.

Someday, I shall tell you other stories, but these are stories for another day.

Though I must finish, I do not really say "good-bye" for in our language there is no word for "good-bye."

Listen, listen and someday you may hear deep within the forest a beating noise, very deep, very faint, and very far away. This is I, Nimosom, beating my drum and sending you a story across the top of the world just as have my fathers since the days when the world was very young.

Postscipt

PRENTICE DOWNES

THE PRECEDING STORIES ARE IN THE FIRST PERSON. THE TELLER IS ADAM Ballantyne, an old Cree Indian who is 'Nimosom' or 'grandfather' and the narrator. Though Adam himself reveals something of his life and background, it may be of some interest to know more, particularly as it is anticipated that the stories themselves may elicit inquiry. Adam Ballantyne was, at the time he told me these stories, a man probably about seventy-five years old. This was in the summer of 1937. I saw him again in the summer of 1947 and he was still quite alive. As he was not a Christian Indian there was no definite record of his birth. He spoke no English and the stories were told to me in his native Cree language. At that time I was sufficiently conversant in that language to grasp a good part of the stories but I was immensely helped on occasion by excellent interpretation. Adam was a member of the Pelican Narrows Band, a forest dwelling, hunting people found at Pelican Lake in far northeastern Saskatchewan, Canada. Though these Indians have long been exposed to the white man and the white man's various religious concepts, as one can see, the more ancient beliefs still persist, at least among such of the old men as Adam. He himself occupies a curious position in the band. Though the younger members are inclined to ridicule his ancient beliefs, when all the white man's religion, his nostrums, painkillers and pills fail, they turn to the old medicine man — Adam.